CGP ♥s Non-Fiction – it's true love...

This Foundation SAT Buster from CGP is perfect for pupils who need some extra support in KS2 English — it's packed with Non-Fiction Reading practice that builds towards the level of the SATs.

There's plenty of help along the way, with tips and example answers to help them get to grips with all the crucial skills.

We've also included fun self-assessment boxes to record how they're doing on each topic — and there's a handy scoresheet at the back!

What CGP is all about

Our sole aim here at CGP is to produce the highest quality books — carefully written, immaculately presented and dangerously close to being funny.

Then we work our socks off to get them out to you — at the cheapest possible prices.

Contents

Published by CGP

Editors: Melissa Gardner, Catherine Heygate, Katya Parkes, Rebecca Russell, Sean Walsh

ISBN: 978 1 78908 423 8

With thanks to Izzy Bowen and Alison Griffin for the proofreading.
With thanks to Emily Smith for the copyright research.

Printed by Elanders Ltd, Newcastle upon Tyne.
Clipart from Corel®

Based on the classic CGP style created by Richard Parsons.

WHY DO ELEPHANTS LOOK LIKE ELEPHANTS?

If you've ever seen an elephant on TV or at the zoo, you might have wondered why these giant grey animals look the way they do.

Elephants are unique and amazing creatures. They are the largest land animals on Earth. They are also thought to be the most intelligent mammals in the world after the great apes (a group of animals which includes humans, gorillas and chimpanzees).

Elephants have special features that help them to survive — just like all other animals. For example, giraffes have long necks so that they can reach food at the tops of trees. Polar bears are furry to keep them warm in freezing temperatures. Owls are often brown or grey to help them blend in with the trees around them. These special features are called adaptations.

So why do elephants look like elephants? With their sharp tusks, long trunks and flappy ears, you might think elephants look a little bit unusual, but each of these features has a very special use.

TUSKS

Elephants use their tusks as handy tools. Tusks help them to strip the bark off trees for food and to dig in the ground to look for water. They also use their tusks to fight off other elephants when necessary.

An elephant's tusks are actually enormous teeth. They can grow to be over six feet long — that's bigger than the height of an average adult man! Tusks are an elephant's incisor teeth. Humans have incisors too — they are the teeth at the front of our mouths that we use to bite through food and cut it into small pieces.

Keep turning... ➡

Why Do Elephants Look Like Elephants?

This text is all about elephants. It contains information about why elephants look the way they do, and how they're able to use their bodies to do lots of useful things.

What to do

1) Unfold the pages and read **Why Do Elephants Look Like Elephants?**

2) Read it through one more time to make sure you've got the hang of it.

3) Once you've read it through twice, have a go at the questions.

Turn the page. ➡️

TRUNK

An elephant's trunk is a very useful thing. Firstly, it's a nose. Elephants can use their trunks to smell something that is almost 20 kilometres away. It could take you about 4 hours of non-stop walking to travel 20 kilometres, so that's a pretty long way.

A trunk is more than just a nose, though. Elephants use their trunks like we use our hands. Trunks are very useful for reaching for things, picking things up, carrying things and throwing things.

Many scientists believe that elephants use their trunks to comfort other elephants that are upset or scared. Of course, it's impossible to know what animals are really thinking, but it seems like elephants use their trunks in the same way that we might use our arms to hug a family member who is feeling down.

EARS

Elephants live in parts of Africa and Southeast Asia where the weather can get very warm. Their ears help them to keep cool, though. An elephant's ears are quite thin and are full of lots of little blood vessels. When they get too warm, elephants flap their ears back and forth, which cools down the blood. This cool blood is then carried all around the elephant's body. Amazing, isn't it?

So that's why elephants look like elephants. All of their weird and wonderful features are actually really practical. Their tusks, trunks and ears help them to stay safe, find food and live comfortably in their environment.

Fact Retrieval Questions

FACT RETRIEVAL questions are all about finding information in the text. Think about what you've learned from 'Why Do Elephants Look Like Elephants?', then try these questions.

1) Read the paragraph beginning '**Elephants are unique...**'
   This paragraph tells us that elephants are

   | animals in the 'great apes' group | similar to gorillas and chimpanzees | the largest land animals on Earth | the cleverest animals on Earth |

   Circle your answer.

   _____
   1 mark

2) Read the paragraph beginning '**Elephants have special features...**'
   Why do giraffes have long necks?

   Tick **one** box.

   To keep them warm ☐

   To help them run faster ☐

   To help them blend in ☐

   To help them reach food ☑

   _____
   1 mark

3) Why do elephants dig in the ground?

   Look at the paragraph beginning 'Elephants use their tusks...'

   .... for water ....

   _____
   1 mark

4) Read the paragraph beginning '**An elephant's tusks are actually...**'
   What are tusks?

   | horns | teeth | bones | nails |

   Circle your answer.

   _____
   1 mark

Section 1 — Why Do Elephants Look Like Elephants?   © CGP — not to be photocopied

Here's what you have to do:

In Year 6 you have to take some tests called the SATs.
This book will help you do well in the reading bit of the tests.

The reading paper will test you on eight different reading elements:

2a Word Meanings   **2c** Summarising   **2e** Predictions   **2g** Language

2b Fact Retrieval   **2d** Inferences   **2f** Structure   **2h** Comparisons

These elements are used to see how well you can understand texts.

To help you improve your reading skills, this book has separate question pages for each of the reading elements — so you always know which one you are practising.

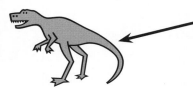 This is a Reading Raptor — it can read and understand even the trickiest non-fiction texts.

Your aim is to become a Reading Raptor.

Work through the questions in the book. When you finish a section, add up your marks and write them in the scoresheet at the end of the book.

Then, put a tick in the box at the end of the topic to show how you got on.

 If you got a lot of questions wrong, put a tick in the circle on the left. Don't worry — every Reading Raptor has to start somewhere. Read the texts again carefully, then have another go.

If you're nearly there but you're still a bit wobbly on some questions, put a tick in the middle circle. Ask your teacher to help you work out the areas you need more practice on.

 If you felt really confident and got nearly all the answers right, tick the circle on the right.

Congratulations — you're a Reading Raptor!

2b	# Fact Retrieval Questions

5) According to the text, how long can an elephant's tusks grow to be?

...............6ft...

1 mark

6) According to the text, what do elephants use their trunks for? Tick **one** box.

to smell [✓]   to dig [ ]

to taste [ ]   to fight [ ]

Look in the section called 'Trunk' if you need some help.

1 mark

7) Read the paragraph beginning **'Elephants live in parts of Africa...'**
    What do elephants do to cool themselves down? Tick **one** box.

They drink lots of water. [ ]

They strip the bark from trees. [ ]

They flap their ears back and forth. [✓]

They go for a swim in a river. [ ]

1 mark

8) Put a tick in the correct box to show whether each statement is true or false.
    The first one has been done for you.

	True	False
Elephants live in North Asia.		✓
Elephants' ears are very thick.		✓
Elephants have lots of blood vessels in their ears.	✓	

1 mark

Reading Raptors can retrieve facts faster than you can say "egg". How did you find these questions?

Section 1 — Why Do Elephants Look Like Elephants?

Inference Questions

2d

Texts don't always make things obvious to the reader, so INFERENCE questions are about figuring out hidden meanings. Read through the text carefully, then answer these questions.

1) Read the paragraph beginning **'Elephants are unique...'**
   Find and copy a phrase which suggests that people aren't exactly sure how intelligent elephants are.

   ....

   1 mark

2) Read the paragraph beginning **'So why do elephants...'**
   The writer's description suggests that

   Look at the words the writer uses to describe elephants.

elephants don't look like other animals	elephants are similar to many animals	elephants are very smart	elephants are very strong

   Circle your answer.

   1 mark

3) Read the paragraph beginning **'Elephants use their tusks...'**
   This paragraph suggests that elephant tusks are

   Think about how elephants use their tusks.

thin	strong	bendy	weak

   Circle your answer.

   1 mark

4) **'They also use their tusks to fight off other elephants when necessary.'**
   What does **'when necessary'** suggest about elephants? Tick **one** box.

   They are bad at fighting. ☐

   They are good at fighting. ☐

   They only fight when they need to. ☐

   They enjoy fighting other elephants. ☐

   1 mark

| 2d | **Inference Questions** |

5) How can you tell that elephants have a good sense of smell?

Look at the information you're given in 'Trunk'.

....

....

_____
1 mark

6) **'A trunk is more than just a nose, though.'**

What do you think the writer means by **'more than just a nose'**? Tick **one** box.

Trunks are much bigger than human noses. ☐

Trunks are used for other things apart from smelling. ☐

An elephant's trunk doesn't have many uses. ☐

Elephants have more than one nose. ☐

Think about where this phrase comes in the text.

_____
1 mark

7) Read the paragraph beginning **'Many scientists believe that...'**

Which word best matches the writer's description of elephants in this paragraph?

| cruel | caring | brave | boring |

Circle your answer.

_____
1 mark

8) Put a tick in the correct box to show whether each statement is a fact or an opinion. The first one has been done for you.

	Fact	Opinion
Humans have incisor teeth.	✓	
Elephants use their trunks to lift things.	✓	
The way elephants use their ears is amazing.		✓

_____
1 mark

Reading Raptors are better at inference questions than any other type of dinosaur. How did you get on?

Section 1 — Why Do Elephants Look Like Elephants?

Word Meaning Questions

It's time for WORD MEANING questions, so get your vocabulary hat on. These questions are all about what individual words in the text mean. See how you get on with them.

1) **'...each of these features has a very special use.'**
   What does the word **'special'** mean in this sentence? Tick **one** box.

   popular ☐   important ☐

   difficult ☐   comfortable ☐

   Think about how these features help elephants.

   1 mark

2) Read the paragraph beginning **'An elephant's tusks are actually...'**
   Find and copy **one** word which could be replaced with the word 'huge'.

   ....

   1 mark

3) **'...elephants use their trunks to comfort other elephants...'**
   Which word is closest in meaning to the word **'comfort'**? Tick **one** box.

   cheer up ☐   annoy ☐

   fight ☐   tickle ☐

   Use the rest of the paragraph to help you work this one out.

   1 mark

4) **'All of their weird and wonderful features are actually really practical.'**
   What does **'practical'** mean in this sentence? Circle your answer.

   | strange | useful | amazing | pointless |

   1 mark

Reading Raptors answer word meaning questions while standing on their heads. How did you find these?

Section 1 — Why Do Elephants Look Like Elephants?   © CGP — not to be photocopied

Summary Questions

SUMMARY questions get you to think about the main points that the text is making. Have another read over 'Why Do Elephants Look Like Elephants?', then try these questions.

1)   What is the main message of the text? Tick **one** box.

There's no reason why elephants look the way they do.   ☐

Elephants know when other elephants are upset.   ☐

An elephant's most important feature is its trunk.   ☐

Elephants use their special features to help them survive.   ☐

_____
1 mark

2)   The title of the text is '**Why Do Elephants Look Like Elephants?**'.
Suggest a different title you could use for the text.

....
_____
1 mark

Language Question

For LANGUAGE questions, you need to think about why a writer chose to use certain words, and the effect that they have on the reader. Take a look at this question and give it a go.

1)   Read the paragraph beginning '**Elephants are unique...**'
How can you tell that the writer finds elephants impressive?

> *Think about the words the writer uses to describe elephants.*

....

....
_____
1 mark

*Reading Raptors can juggle six oranges at a time.
How did you do with these questions? Tick one.*

Fact Retrieval Questions

2b

FACT RETRIEVAL questions get you to pick out pieces of information from the text. Now that you've read 'Paw-sitively Brilliant', see how you get on with these questions.

1) What does The Sunshine Shelter do? Tick **one** box.

It looks after animals. ☐

It gives food to the homeless. ☐

It takes care of poorly people. ☐

It looks after children. ☐

Have a look at the introduction if you need some help.

1 mark

2) Read the section called **'Long Walks on the Beach'**.

After the sponsored dog walk, everyone

| had a picnic | went swimming in the sea | got their faces painted | had a barbecue by the pier |

Circle your answer.

1 mark

3) Read the section called **'Kids About Town'**.

Where were the posters that Year 3 made about the animal shelter displayed?

....

1 mark

4) Give the names of **two** businesses that donated prizes for the Year 3 raffle.

....

....

2 marks

Keep turning...

Paw-sitively Brilliant:
Schoolchildren Raise Hundreds of Pounds for Animal Charity

This week, hard-working pupils from Foxglove Junior School raised more than £600 for The Sunshine Shelter — a charity that looks after abandoned or injured animals.

It's been a busy week for children at Foxglove Junior School. They have been working non-stop to raise money for local animal charity, The Sunshine Shelter.

Every year group in the school took part in different activities to help raise money and inform people about the shelter's work.

LONG WALKS ON THE BEACH

Year 6 kicked off the fundraising efforts with a sponsored dog walk. Children, parents and members of the public brought their dogs along on Sunday for a friendly and fun walk along the beach. The forecast for Sunday was poor, so walkers came prepared with their umbrellas and waterproof jackets. Thankfully, the weather stayed warm and dry all day. The walk ended with a barbecue by the pier.

KIDS ABOUT TOWN

On Monday, Year 3 pupils made posters telling people about the shelter's work. These are being put up in shop windows in the town centre.

Spud, who belongs to Year 6 pupil Amala Ayoade, was a big fan of the sponsored walk.

Year 3 also raised money by selling raffle tickets to friends and family. Local businesses, including Candice's Curls, The Clear Window Company and Foxglove Sweet Shop, donated several prizes for the raffle.

RISING TO THE OCCASION

Foxglove Infant School pupils also got to join in with the fun on Thursday, when Year 5 hosted a bake sale in the infant school. Pupils and teachers enjoyed homemade cakes and biscuits in exchange for a small contribution towards the charity.

Infant pupils also got to meet some of the birds, rabbits and guinea pigs that live at the shelter, and learned about how to care for them. The pupils were very excited to meet the small pets, and two rabbits and a parrot were later adopted by infant pupils — with their parents' permission, of course.

DRESSED FOR SUCCESS

The week ended in style with a non-uniform day on Friday, organised by Year 4 pupils. Children were encouraged to wear outfits inspired by their favourite animals. Cats, dogs, mice and (to much surprise) lobsters were among the most popular choices.

In the afternoon, children from Year 4 offered face painting to the rest of the school. Eager pupils queued for almost an hour to get animal-themed artwork on their faces.

"It was really fun," said one of the Year 4 pupils, Bethany Turner. "I love art, so it was great to get to paint people's faces. The dog walk on Sunday was the best, though. My dad and I enjoyed walking my dog, Charlie. I'm glad that the money we raised will help other animals like Charlie."

REAL IMPACTS

At the end of the week, the school worked out that they had raised

The bake sale proved very successful and raised over £100.

a total of £642.87 from all the activities. "I am very proud of each and every one of my pupils," said the head teacher of Foxglove Junior School, Mrs Knight. "They have all put in so much effort and raised lots of money for a very good cause."

The money raised will go towards the new puppy unit that is now under construction at The Sunshine Shelter.

The manager of The Sunshine Shelter, Karim Rashid, told reporters, "We are very impressed by the kindness shown by the pupils of Foxglove Junior School and the rest of the community. This money will make such a big difference for all of the animals we're looking after."

If you would like to adopt an animal or donate money to The Sunshine Shelter, you can do so in person, by telephone or online.

Paw-sitively Brilliant

This piece of non-fiction is a newspaper article about a school that raised money for a local animal charity. The text includes information about all the different ways the pupils raised the money, and how it will help the animal shelter.

What to do

1) Unfold the pages, and read the article **Paw-sitively Brilliant**.

2) Then read it again. This will help make sure you understand everything and know exactly what's going on.

3) Once you've finished that, have a crack at the questions.

Turn the page. ➡

Fact Retrieval Questions

2b

Look in the section called 'Dressed for Success'.

5) What **two** fundraising activities did Year 4 organise?

....

....

2 marks

6) According to the text, who is Mrs Knight? Circle your answer.

| the Year 4 teacher | a parent | the head teacher | the head of the shelter |

1 mark

7) Put a tick in the correct box to show whether each statement is true or false. The first one has been done for you.

	True	False
Bethany Turner is in Year 4.	✓	
Bethany Turner's dog is called Chester.		
The pupils raised over £800 for charity.		

1 mark

8) How will The Sunshine Shelter use the money that was raised? Tick **one** box.

It will be used for rescuing injured birds. ☐

It will be given to the new puppy unit. ☐

It will help the shelter care for abandoned cats. ☐

It will be used to teach people about the shelter. ☐

1 mark

Reading Raptors eat facts for breakfast. They're very tasty. How did you get on with these questions?

© CGP — not to be photocopied

Section 2 — Paw-sitively Brilliant

Inference Questions

To answer INFERENCE questions, you need to think carefully about what the text is really saying. Read 'Paw-sitively Brilliant' again and then see how you get on with these questions.

1) Read the paragraph beginning **'It's been...'**
   How can you tell that the pupils have been working hard?

   ....

   1 mark

2) How can you tell that people were worried it might rain on Sunday?

   Look at the information you're given in the section called 'Long Walks on the Beach'.

   ....

   ....

   1 mark

3) Read the paragraph beginning **'Year 3 also raised money...'**
   Choose the option that best describes the local businesses. Tick **one** box.

   They aren't interested in the animal shelter. ☐

   They are all businesses related to animals. ☐

   They want to support the animal shelter. ☐

   They don't want to help the local community. ☐

   1 mark

4) a) Do you think the infant pupils enjoyed seeing the small pets from the shelter? Tick **one** box.

   Read the paragraph beginning 'Infant pupils also got to meet...'

   Yes ☐   No ☐

   1 mark

   b) Find and copy **one** piece of evidence from the text to support your answer.

   ....

   1 mark

2d **Inference Questions**

5) Read the paragraph beginning '**The week ended in style...**'
Find and copy a phrase which suggests that lobsters were an unexpected choice of outfit.

....

1 mark

6) '**Eager pupils queued for almost an hour...**'
What does this tell you about the face painting? Tick **one** box.

Think about what the word 'eager' might suggest.

The face painting was very popular. ☐

Only a few people got their faces painted. ☐

The pupils painted faces all day. ☐

People didn't want to get their faces painted. ☐

1 mark

7) Read the paragraph beginning '"**It was really fun...**'
How can you tell that Bethany Turner's favourite activity was the sponsored dog walk?

....

1 mark

8) Read the paragraph beginning '**The manager of The Sunshine Shelter...**'
This paragraph suggests that Karim Rashid is

Look at the language he uses.

| thankful | shocked | entertained | hopeful |

Circle your answer.

1 mark

Reading Raptors like to do inference questions hanging upside down by their toes. How did you find these?

Word Meaning Questions

WORD MEANING questions are all about what words mean, funnily enough. If you're not sure what a word means, use the sentence around it to help you work it out. Let's have a go.

1) **'...to help raise money and inform people about the shelter's work.'**
What does the word **'inform'** mean in this sentence? Circle your answer.

ask	learn	tell	send

_____
1 mark

2) **'...Year 5 hosted a bake sale in the infant school.'**
What does the word **'hosted'** mean in this sentence? Tick **one** box.

held ☐   cancelled ☐

invented ☐   visited ☐

Think about what happens in the rest of the paragraph.

_____
1 mark

3) Read the paragraph beginning **'At the end of the week...'**
Find and copy a phrase which could be replaced with the word 'calculated'.

....
1 mark

4) **'...the new puppy unit that is now under construction...'**
What does **'under construction'** mean in this sentence? Circle your answer.

open	underground	finished	being built

_____
1 mark

Reading Raptors love figuring out what words mean. How did you get on with these questions?

⋮ *The last few questions on Paw-sitively Brilliant are under here.* ➡

Section 2 — Paw-sitively Brilliant   *© CGP — not to be photocopied*

If you want to do something more energetic, the outdoors is the place to be. You can walk up hills, fly a kite on the beach or go exploring. Take a bike or scooter and you'll be able to explore much further than you can on foot. Sport is another great way to get outdoors. If you're interested in sports like football, cricket, rugby or hockey, there might be a local club you can join, or maybe you could organise a team with your friends.

Finally, if you're interested in wildlife, there are things you can do wherever you are in the country. You could take up birdwatching and learn to identify different types of birds in your local area. Setting up feeders will help to attract birds to your garden or any other outdoor space. If you want to see different kinds of creatures too, you could build small shelters using wood, stones, bricks or cardboard so that insects and other local wildlife have a place to live. This will give them somewhere safe to make their home, and you'll get the chance to see them up close.

So there you have it — you don't have to be indoors to have fun or enjoy your hobbies. Whatever the time of year, wherever you are and whatever you're interested in, there's something for you to do outdoors. So head outside and have an adventure today.

 Open the flap for the start of the text.

Great Adventures in the Great Outdoors

This piece of non-fiction is all about the fun things you can do outdoors. It talks about why being outside is good for you, and suggests lots of activities to get you exploring the great outdoors.

What to do

1) Read **Great Adventures in the Great Outdoors**.

2) Then read it through one more time. This will make sure you've read and understood as much as possible.

3) Once you've read it twice, see how you get on with the questions.

Great Adventures in the Great Outdoors

When you're thinking about what to do at the weekend, what's the first thing that comes to mind? Maybe it's watching TV, playing a video game or reading. Maybe you enjoy a hobby, like playing an instrument, drawing or baking. Whatever you enjoy doing, chances are it'll be something you do indoors. So, does that mean you need to be inside to have fun?

According to a recent study, four out of five children don't feel in touch with nature. With so much to do indoors, these numbers are not unexpected. There are lots of benefits to spending time outdoors, though — it can make you feel healthier, happier and even less lonely. Read on for some ideas on where to go and what to do to have your own outdoor adventure.

The text continues over the page. ➡

A Permanent Playground

Summer is always a popular time to get outdoors and have fun because it's warmer and usually less rainy than the rest of the year. There's no need to just stay indoors in spring, autumn and winter, though — each season brings its own exciting things to see and do. If you can find a horse chestnut tree, autumn can be a great time for collecting conkers. In the winter months, frost or snow turns the outdoors into a winter wonderland. Spring is a great time to get out into the fresh air and see hundreds of beautiful flowers begin to bloom.

Options Outdoors

We say 'outdoors' like it's all one place, but in reality the outdoors is made up of millions of different spaces. Some people will thoroughly enjoy spending time in their own back garden and won't want to go further than that. For others, their back garden is just the beginning. Maybe you already know of a spot nearby that you'd like to explore — a park, a field, some woodland, a beach. If not, you could investigate what your local area has to offer. There are plenty of options to suit everyone. Wherever you decide to go, make sure you always get an adult to accompany you. Even when you're old enough to be out alone, make sure that someone responsible always knows where you are.

Activities for Everyone

There are so many things you can do outside, and many of them need little or no preparation. You could watch the sun rise or set, go cloud watching or go stargazing. You could use materials you find outside to create a natural artwork or make a den. Trying to do things you normally do inside, but doing them outdoors can make them more fun — why not turn your lunch into a picnic, or take your book or handheld device out into the fresh air?

← *Keep turning...*

Summary Questions

For SUMMARY questions, you need to think about the main points of the text, rather than the tiny details. Put your summarising skills to the test and try these questions.

1) The section called **'Dressed for Success'** is about

| the Year 5 bake sale | face painting | Bethany Turner's dog | Year 4's fundraising |

Circle your answer.

_____
1 mark

2) Which of these sentences is the main idea of the section called **'Real Impacts'**? Tick **one** box.

Look carefully at the section and think about what it's talking about.

The fundraising was really enjoyable. ☐

Pupils learned a lot about the shelter's work. ☐

Parents helped out with the fundraising. ☐

The money raised by the pupils will help animals. ☐

_____
1 mark

Prediction Question

You don't need magic powers to answer PREDICTION questions, you just need to use the information in the text to suggest what might happen in the future. Have a crack at this one.

1) Do you think people will get involved with the charity after reading this article?
Explain your answer, making sure you refer to the text.

Give as much detail as you can.

....

....

....

_____
2 marks

Reading Raptors dream about summary and prediction questions every night. How did you get on with these?

 2b

Fact Retrieval Questions

For FACT RETRIEVAL questions, you need to hunt down specific pieces of information in the text. Have a go at the questions below and see how you do.

1) Read the paragraph beginning **'When you're thinking about...'**
   Which of these things is **not** listed as a hobby?

   Make sure you read the question carefully.

   | playing an instrument | baking | painting | drawing |

   Circle your answer.

   _____
   1 mark

2) According to the text, how many children don't feel in touch with nature? Tick **one** box.

   You'll find the answer in the second paragraph of the text.

   a few ☐   less than half ☐

   four out of five ☐   ten out of ten ☐

   _____
   1 mark

3) Read the paragraph beginning **'According to a recent study...'**
   Based on the text, give **one** benefit of spending time outdoors.

   ....
   _____
   1 mark

4) Read the section called **'A Permanent Playground'**.
   According to this section, why is summer a popular time to be outdoors?

   | You can find conkers. | It's warmer and drier. | There's no school. | It's very rainy. |

   Circle your answer.

   _____
   1 mark

Fact Retrieval Questions

2b

5) Read the section called '**Options Outdoors**'.
   Give **two** examples of places that you could explore.

   ....

   ....

   2 marks

6) Read the paragraph beginning '**There are so many things...**'
   According to this paragraph, how could you use materials that you find outside?

   Tick **one** box.

   You could make a den.   ☐

   You could put them in the bin.   ☐

   You could make a bird feeder.   ☐

   You could have a picnic.   ☐

   Careful — the text mentions a few of these things.

   1 mark

7) Read the paragraph beginning '**Finally, if you're interested in wildlife...**'
   What would you learn if you took up birdwatching? Circle your answer.

   | **how to attract birds** | **how to protect birds** | **how to catch birds** | **how to identify birds** |

   1 mark

8) '**Setting up feeders will help to attract birds...**'
   Based on the text, give **one** other way that you could attract wildlife
   to your garden.

   ....

   1 mark

Reading Raptors have sensors in their tails to help them find facts. How did you get on with these questions?

Section 3 — Great Adventures in the Great Outdoors

Inference Questions

It's time to solve some mysteries! INFERENCE questions are all about figuring out what the words in the text are really saying. Use your detective skills and give these questions a go.

1) Read the paragraph beginning **'According to a recent study...'**
   The phrase **'children don't feel in touch with nature'** suggests that young people

don't touch animals	**don't spend much time outdoors**	**know a lot about wildlife**	**are outside all the time**

   Circle your answer.

   _____
   1 mark

2) Read the section called **'A Permanent Playground'**.
   Find and copy a word which suggests that summer isn't always drier than other seasons.

   ....

   _____
   1 mark

3) **'...frost or snow turns the outdoors into a winter wonderland.'**
   This sentence suggests that during winter, the outdoors is

beautiful	**weird**	**gloomy**	**dangerous**

   Circle your answer.

   _____
   1 mark

4) **'For others, their back garden is just the beginning.'**
   What does the phrase **'is just the beginning'** suggest? Tick **one** box.

   Their back garden has just been completed. ☐

   They don't like to travel very far. ☐

   They want to explore further than their garden. ☐

   They like to spend time in their garden. ☐

   Look at what comes around this in the text.

   _____
   1 mark

Section 3 — Great Adventures in the Great Outdoors   *© CGP — not to be photocopied*

Inference Questions

5) **'There are so many things you can do outside, and many of them need little or no preparation.'**
What does this suggest about outdoor activities? Circle your answer.

| They are easy to do. | There aren't very many. | You need lots of equipment. | They're hard to plan. |

_____
1 mark

6) Read the paragraph beginning **'If you want to do something...'**
What evidence is there that travelling by bike or scooter is faster than walking?

....

....

_____
1 mark

7) Put a tick in the correct box to show whether each statement is a fact or an opinion.
The first one has been done for you.

	Fact	Opinion
Every season is exciting.		✓
Conkers come from horse chestnut trees.		
Picnics are more fun than eating indoors.		

_____
1 mark

8) Read the paragraph beginning **'Finally, if you're interested in wildlife...'**
How can you tell that shelters protect wildlife from danger?

....

_____
1 mark

Reading Raptors write love songs about inference questions. They're really beautiful. How did you do?

Word Meaning Questions

WORD MEANING questions put your vocabulary skills to the test — you'll have to figure out what specific words in the text mean. See how you get on with the questions below.

1) **'With so much to do indoors, these numbers are not unexpected.'**
   Circle the word closest in meaning to the word **'unexpected'**.

terrifying	likely	true	surprising

   1 mark

2) **'We say 'outdoors' like it's all one place, but in reality, the outdoors is made up of millions of different spaces.'**
   What does the phrase **'in reality'** mean in this sentence? Tick **one** box.

   outside ☐   sometimes ☐

   actually ☐   luckily ☐

   Think about which word would make sense in the sentence.

   1 mark

3) **'If you want to do something more energetic, the outdoors is the place to be.'**
   Which word in this sentence could be replaced with the word 'active'?

   ....

   1 mark

4) **'...learn to identify different types of birds.'**
   What does the word **'identify'** mean in this sentence?

   ....

   1 mark

Reading Raptors have laser eyes. Just a fun fact. How did you get on with these questions? Tick one.   ○✓ ○✓ ○✓

The last few questions on Great Adventures... are under here. ➤

Snow may seem like a strange choice of building material — especially in freezing climates. However, even snow igloos provide shelter from the cold wind and trap in enough heat to keep the people inside cosy and warm.

Some people imagine the Inuit lived in snow igloos all the time, but this isn't strictly true. The Inuit could build these sturdy snow houses with ease, but they were usually used as temporary shelters during winter, rather than permanent homes. In the summer months, the Inuit slept in tents made of animal skins.

The Inuit Today

Nowadays, Inuit culture is evolving. Instead of moving around from place to place, many Inuit people have settled in villages and built permanent homes. Many people also take advantage of modern technology to make their lives easier. Some Inuit people now prefer to travel across the snow using snowmobiles instead of sledges. This allows them to make journeys without having to stop along the way to let the huskies rest and eat.

A snowmobile

Some Inuit people now have paid jobs and use the money they earn to pay for food and clothes from shops, as well as other modern comforts like electricity and the internet.

However, not everyone is as keen to modernise all aspects of Inuit life. Many families continue to teach their children traditional Inuit skills, such as hunting and making clothes from animal skins.

 Open the flap for the start of the text.

The Inuit People

This text is all about a group of people called the Inuit. They live in some of the coldest parts of the world, and this text looks at a few of the ways they have adapted to their chilly environment.

What to do

1) Read the text **The Inuit People**.

2) Then give it another read. This will make sure you understand it all, even the little details.

3) Once you know what the text is all about, have a go at the questions.

The Inuit People

The Inuit are a group of people who live in the snowy regions of Greenland, Alaska* and northern Canada. The Inuit have their own history, languages and traditions.

If you were to meet an Inuk (a member of the Inuit people) today, their life might seem quite similar to yours. However, Inuit people have been around for thousands of years, and their way of life used to be very different. They developed many clever ways of finding food, travelling and making shelter.

Living Off the Land

The Inuit people used to be hunter-gatherers, which meant that they found all the food they needed from the land around them. They hunted animals such as seals, reindeer and even polar bears.

Hunters could be away from their families for days at a time on dangerous hunting trips, but it was worth it. The animals they caught provided them with food, and the Inuit also used the animals' skins to make clothes, shoes and tents. Even the bones of the animals came in handy for making tools.

As the Inuit could find or make everything they needed, money didn't exist in traditional Inuit culture.

An Inuit woman wearing a coat made of animal skins.

Glossary

Alaska — the most northern state in the USA

The text continues over the page. ➡

Section 4 — The Inuit People

Huskies

Getting Around

Most Inuit people live very far north, meaning that the land is usually covered in snow and ice. In the past, the Inuit built wooden sledges in order to transport themselves and their supplies across this challenging landscape. These sledges were pulled by packs of dogs. Huskies were often used, as they are a breed of dog that have been specially bred to pull heavy sledges. They have thick fur to keep them warm in the freezing temperatures.

The Inuit also built narrow boats called kayaks. These boats were small and swift, which allowed the Inuit to hunt for animals, such as fish and seals, in the water.

Home Sweet Home

A snow igloo

Inuit people were traditionally nomadic, meaning they moved around and didn't live in one place for very long. They travelled to different places depending on the seasons to make sure they could find enough food.

The Inuit lived in homes called igloos. When we imagine an igloo, we usually think of a dome-shaped shelter made of snow. However, the word 'iglu' in Inuktitut* just means house, so the Inuit call any home an igloo — whether it's made from snow, animals' skins or brick.

Glossary

Inuktitut — one of the main Inuit languages

31

2c

Summary Questions

SUMMARY questions are all about working out the main ideas in different parts of the text. Give the text another read through, then give these questions a try.

1) Put these summaries of paragraphs in the order they happen in the text.
The first one has been done for you.

There are many places to explore outdoors. [ ]

Children spend a lot of time indoors. [1]

How to attract animals to your garden. [ ]

There's something to do outdoors in every season. [ ]

Read each paragraph again, stopping to think about the main idea in each one.

_____
1 mark

2) Read the section called '**Activities for Everyone**'.
Which sentence would you use to summarise this section? Circle your answer.

Being outside is good for your health.	**People spend a lot of time indoors.**	**There are lots of activities to do outdoors.**	**People should play more sports.**

_____
1 mark

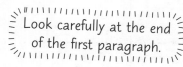

2f

Structure Question

STRUCTURE questions ask you to look at the order of the text, and think about how different sections work together. Have a go at this question and see how you get on.

1) How does the last paragraph of the text link back to the first paragraph?

Look carefully at the end of the first paragraph.

....

....

_____
1 mark

Reading Raptors can't make the bed — their arms are too short. Anyway, how did you find these questions?

© CGP — not to be photocopied   *Section 3 — Great Adventures in the Great Outdoors*

Fact Retrieval Questions

FACT RETRIEVAL questions are about locating key bits of information in the text. Read 'The Inuit People' again, then have a go at these questions.

1) According to the introduction, what is a member of the Inuit called?

| an Inu | an Inuit | an Inuk | the Inuits |

Circle your answer.

_____
1 mark

2) Read the paragraph beginning **'Hunters could be away...'**
How long could hunters be away on hunting trips for? Tick **one** box.

days ☐   several hours ☐

months ☐   weeks at a time ☐

_____
1 mark

3) Give **two** things that the Inuit used animals for apart from food.

....

....
_____
2 marks

4) What type of dog has been bred to pull sledges?

Look at the section called 'Getting Around'.

....
_____
1 mark

5) Read the paragraph beginning **'The Inuit also built...'**
Give **one** animal that the Inuit hunted in the water.

....
_____
1 mark

Fact Retrieval Questions

2b

6) Why did the Inuit move around depending on the seasons?

Tick **one** box.

for a change of scenery ☐

to find enough food ☐

to find somewhere warmer ☐

to find better snow ☐

Read the paragraph beginning 'Inuit people were traditionally nomadic...'

1 mark

7) Read the paragraph beginning **'Some people imagine the Inuit...'**
    Where did the Inuit sleep during the summer? Circle your answer.

| snow igloos | permanent homes | tents made of canvas | tents made of animal skins |

1 mark

8) Read the section called **'The Inuit Today'**.
    Based on the text, give **one** thing that the Inuit now use money to pay for.

    ....

1 mark

9) Put a tick in the correct box to show whether each statement is true or false.

	True	False
Some Inuit people live in Greenland.		
Inuktitut is the only Inuit language.		
Snow igloos are very cold inside.		

1 mark

How many Reading Raptors does it take to retrieve a fact? Just one. They're that good. How did you do?

Inference Questions

INFERENCE questions ask you to look beyond the words and figure out exactly what a text means. Read the text carefully, then see how you get on with these questions.

1) Read the paragraph beginning **'The Inuit are a group of people...'**
   Find and copy a phrase which suggests that the Inuit live in cold places.

   ....

   1 mark

2) Read the paragraph beginning **'Hunters could be away...'**
   What does this paragraph suggest about how the Inuit used the animals
   that they hunted?

They sold them.	They gave them as gifts.	They threw a lot of the animal away.	They used many parts of the animal.

   Circle your answer.

   1 mark

3) Why didn't money exist in traditional Inuit culture? Tick **one** box.

   It was against the law. ☐

   The Inuit didn't like it. ☐

   The Inuit didn't need to buy anything. ☐

   No one had thought of it. ☐

   If you're not sure, go back to the section called 'Living Off the Land'.

   1 mark

4) Look at the paragraph beginning **'Most Inuit people live...'**
   This paragraph suggests that huskies are

lazy	strong	small	friendly

   Circle your answer.

   1 mark

Inference Questions

2d

5) Read the paragraph beginning **'Some people imagine the Inuit...'**
What evidence is there that the Inuit were experts at building snow igloos?

....

1 mark

6) Why do you think the Inuit didn't build permanent houses? Tick **one** box.

They were always moving around. ☐

They didn't know how. ☐

They didn't have the materials. ☐

The houses kept falling down. ☐

1 mark

7) Read the paragraph beginning **'Nowadays, Inuit culture is evolving.'**
Why do some Inuit people use snowmobiles instead of sledges?

| Snowmobiles are faster. | They don't have dogs. | Snowmobiles are expensive. | They got bored of sledges. |

Circle your answer.

1 mark

8) Read the paragraph beginning **'However, not everyone is as keen...'**
How can you tell that some Inuit people think it's important to hold on
to traditions?

....

....

1 mark

Reading Raptors can answer inference questions while standing on one leg. How did you find these questions?

Section 4 — The Inuit People

Word Meaning Questions

WORD MEANING questions get you to think about what specific words in the text mean.
You can often use the rest of the sentence around the word to help you figure it out.

1) Read the paragraph beginning **'Most Inuit people live...'**

Find and copy **one** word which could be replaced with the word 'difficult'.

....

1 mark

2) **'These boats were small and swift...'**

What does the word **'swift'** mean in this sentence? Tick **one** box.

quick ☐   slow ☐

long ☐   short ☐

1 mark

3) **'Snow may seem like a strange choice of building material...'**

Circle the word below that is closest in meaning to **'strange'**.

| large | good | peculiar | lucky |

1 mark

4) **'The Inuit could build these sturdy snow houses with ease...'**

What does the word **'sturdy'** mean in this sentence?

....

1 mark

5) **'Nowadays, Inuit culture is evolving.'**

What does **'evolving'** mean in this sentence?

> Think about what the rest
> of the paragraph says.

| closing | disappearing | starting | changing |

Circle your answer.

1 mark

Reading Raptors win the Word Meaning Championships every year. How did you get on with these questions?

Section 4 — The Inuit People

Summary Questions

For SUMMARY questions, you often have to think about how to describe whole sections of the text in just a few words. Keep that in mind when you give these questions a try.

1) The section called **'Getting Around'** is about

| a nomadic lifestyle | transport | modern life | Inuit shelters |

Circle your answer.

_____
1 mark

2) Read from **'The Inuit lived in...'** to **'...made of animal skins.'**
Which of these is a main idea in this part of the text? Circle your answer.

| All igloos are made of snow. | Some things people believe about igloos aren't true. | The Inuit have never lived in snow igloos. | The Inuit travelled by sledge. |

_____
1 mark

 # Comparison Question

For COMPARISON questions, you need to think about similarities and differences in the text. Think about everything you've read in 'The Inuit People', then have a go at this question.

1) Describe how Inuit houses have changed over time.
Use evidence from the text to support your answer.

Try to give as much detail as you can.

....

....

....
_____
2 marks

Reading Raptors can't get enough of summary and comparison questions. How did you find these?

Scoresheet

Great work, you're all finished with this book. Use the answer book to find out how well you did and write your marks in the table below.

	Section 1 – Why Do Elephants Look Like Elephants?	Section 2 – Paw-sitively Brilliant	Section 3 – Great Adventures in the Great Outdoors	Section 4 – The Inuit People	Total
2a Word Meanings	/ 4	/ 4	/ 4	/ 5	/ 17
2b Fact Retrieval	/ 8	/ 10	/ 9	/ 10	/ 37
2c Summarising	/ 2	/ 2	/ 2	/ 2	/ 8
2d Inferences	/ 8	/ 9	/ 8	/ 8	/ 33
2e Predictions		/ 2			/ 2
2f Structure			/ 1		/ 1
2g Language	/ 1				/ 1
2h Comparisons				/ 2	/ 2
Total	/ 23	/ 27	/ 24	/ 27	/ 101

Look at your total score to see how you're doing and where you need more practice:

0 – 45 — Don't worry if you got lots wrong. Revise the reading skills you're struggling with and then have another go at the questions.

46 – 80 — You're doing well. Look back at any reading elements you're struggling with and try the questions again to make sure you're happy with them.

81 – 101 — Good work, you're doing great. Give yourself a pat on the back.